Round up

> **A receipt from a shopping trip, paper and penc**

Choose five items from the receipt. Write each price and add them. How much does it cost to buy all five items?

Round each price to the nearest ten pence. Add the new prices. How close is the approximation to the actual cost? Repeat, rounding each price to the nearest pound.

In class Discuss the differences between costs. Which approximations were furthest from the actual costs? Which were closest? Why are some approximations closer than others?

Word count

> **A person to play with, books, newspapers or magazines, paper and pencils**

Take turns to choose a piece of text ten lines long from a magazine, newspaper or book. Count the number of words in the text. Write down the total and divide it by 10 to find the average number of words in a line.

Compare your averages. The person with the highest average wins.

Have four turns each, using a different magazine, newspaper or book each time.

Play again with the lowest average winning.

In class The children, in pairs, find the average number of words per line in a given book, by counting the number of words in 5, 10, 20, then 25 lines of text. Compare the averages. Are they the same?

Different digits

A dice, paper and pencil

Throw the dice and write down the score.

Throw the dice again, and either add or subtract the number thrown to or from the first answer. Then multiply or divide the new total by 10.

Repeat for 10 more throws of the dice. Can you finish with a number which has 5 different digits and is less than 1000?

In class Play the game in class with pairs taking turns to throw the dice and perform the next operation. Write each stage on the board.

throw 4: 4

throw 2: $4 + 2 = 6, 6 \div 10 = 0.6$

throw 1: $0.6 + 1 = 1.6, 1.6 \times 10 = 16$

throw 3: $16 + 3 = 19, 19 \times 10 = 190$

throw 5: $190 + 5 = 195, 195 \times 10 = 1950$

throw 2: $1950 - 2 = 1948, 1948 \div 10 = 194.8$

throw 3: $194.8 + 3 = 197.8, 197.8 \div 10 = 19.78$

throw 1: $19.78 + 1 = 20.78, 20.78 \times 10 = 207.8$

throw 6: $207.8 + 6 = 213.8, 213.8 \times 10 = 2138$

throw 5: $2138 + 5 = 2143, 2143 \times 10 = 21430$

throw 2: $21430 - 2 = 21428, 21428 \div 10 = 2142.8$

throw 4: $2142.8 + 4 = 2146.8, 2146.8 \div 10 = 214.68$

(less than 1000 and has five different digits)

There and back again

A person to play with, paper and pencils

Take turns to choose two cities and look up the distance between them on the chart.

Write down the cities and calculate the distance from one to the point halfway between them. Calculate the distance to travel from one city to the other and back again.

Have five turns each, choosing different cities each time.

Distance chart in km

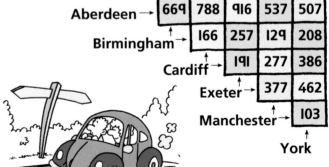

Aberdeen →	669	788	916	537	507
Birmingham →		166	257	129	208
Cardiff →			191	277	386
Exeter →				377	462
Manchester →					103
York →					

In class In pairs the children use distances between the school and local places, e.g. school to swimming pool 4·6 km, to find the halfway distance and the distance there and back.

Near to 1000

A person to talk to, paper and pencil

Write a multiplication of two 2-digit numbers which you think will have an answer close to 1000. One of the numbers must end in a 9.

Explain to someone why you think the answer will be close to 1000. Work out the answer to see how close you were.

Try at least six more different multiplications. How close to 1000 can you get?

In class Discuss how to find multiplications close to a target number. Challenge the children, in pairs, to find a multiplication where one of the numbers ends in 9, with an answer close to 2000. Whose is closest?

Emergency rations

A person to talk to, paper and pencil

Imagine the shops will be closed for two weeks. Choose five items of food or drink to buy to keep in your store cupboard. Ask someone how much the items cost.

Work out how much it will cost to buy 16 of each item. Use a doubling method to help you.

water 55p

55p → £1·10 → £2·20 → £4·40

bones £1·15

£1·15 × 2 = £2·30

£2·30 × 2 = £4·60

In class In pairs, the children work out how much it costs to buy books for a class of 32 children.

Basketball bits

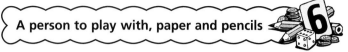

A person to play with, paper and pencils

Take turns to choose a ball and 'shoot' it into a basket. Find the fraction of your ball number shown on the basket. Write the calculation and score the answer.

Keep playing, adding your score each time until each basket has been used. The player with the total score closest to 10, wins.

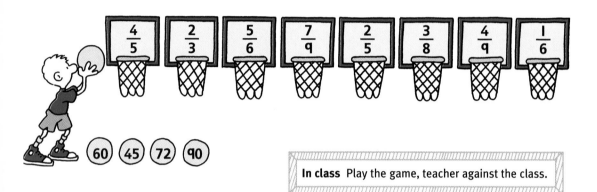

In class Play the game, teacher against the class.

Monthly fractions

Paper and pencil

Choose a cloud. Write the matching number of months in twelfths of the year.

Write the simplest equivalent fraction. Repeat for each cloud.

Months:

without an 'r'

not ending 'ber'

from March to August

beginning with 'J'

with four letters

with five or more letters

In class In pairs the children write the number of hours they spend doing certain things each day, e.g. sleeping, eating meals. They write these as twenty-fourths and reduce them to the simplest possible fraction.

Denominator daze

A person to play with, two sets of number cards (I to I0) (or playing cards, two suits with picture cards removed), paper and pencils

Turn the cards over and spread them out face down. Take turns to pick two cards. Arrange them to make a fraction less than I.

Compare the fractions. Write them down and change them so that they both have the same denominator. Which fraction is largest? Score 2 points each time your fraction is largest. The winner is the first player to I2 points.

In class Play the game, teacher against two class teams. Order all three fractions. The largest wins.

Personalised plates

Paper and pencil

The table shows how much it costs to put letters on a personalised nameplate.

How much would it cost to put your full name on a nameplate? Find how much change you will get if you pay with pound coins.

Try the names of some of your friends or family. Work out how much each nameplate costs and how much change there will be if paid for with pound coins. Can you find a name that costs an exact number of pounds?

12p	15p	18p	19p	25p	29p
A	B	C	D		
E	F	G	H		
I	J	K	L	M	N
O	P	Q	R	S	T
U	V	W	X	Y	Z

Mary Ann Davies = £2·46, pay £3, receive 54p change.

In class Give the names of some famous people (actors, singers, etc.) for the children to work out the cost of their nameplates. Whose name is most expensive?

Target zero

> A counter or coin, paper and pencil

Place a counter or coin on 'Start'. You have 0 points. Move the counter one square at a time across or down (but not diagonally) to move around the jungle.

Write down the numbers you land on. If the square is shaded, you gain that number of points. If the square is white, you lose that number of points. Keep moving, adding and subtracting points, until you reach 'Finish'.

Try to leave the jungle with as close to 0 points as possible. Try different routes. How close can you get?

Start	24	36	29	45	
	39	26	58	23	
	35	56	27	49	
	52	47	28	19	Finish

In class Discuss the best routes through the grid. Repeat for a grid with different numbers.

Turning turtle

> A person to play with, paper and pencils

Take turns to choose two turtle numbers. Subtract the numbers in your head and write down the answer.

Your partner must decide which turtle numbers you chose. Score two points if you subtracted the numbers correctly.

Continue until one player has scored twelve points.

In class Write seven numbers on the board. Choose a child to subtract two numbers and say the answer. The others work out which numbers were subtracted. Discuss the methods they used to subtract.

Common enough

A person to play with, paper and pencils

Take turns to choose two yo-yo numbers and write their lowest common multiple.

Find the lowest common multiple for each pair of yo-yo numbers – there are fifteen pairs in all. How many of the fifteen lowest common multiples are over 50?

In class On the board, write the numbers 4, 5, 7, 8, 12, 20. The children find the lowest common multiple for each pair of numbers. How many of these lowest common multiples are over 50?

Dividing scores

A person to play with, a dice, paper and pencils

Take turns to throw the dice three times and make a 3-digit number. Check your number to see if it is divisible by 3, 5, 6, 9 or 25. Score the points shown in the table.

Have five turns each, adding your score each time. The player with the highest total score wins.

Divisible by	Score
3	2
5	6
6	8
9	10
25	20

In class Play the game, teacher against the class.

Lunch money

> Paper and pencil

Choose some things from the canteen for lunch. Write down the cost of each item and add up the total cost.

How much money would you spend if you ate the same lunch every day for 10 days? How much for 100 days? How much for 1000 days?

Choose a different lunch and repeat.

In class Compare costs and discuss what would be the best value lunch.

10p jackpot

> A counter or coin, paper and pencil

Place the counter or coin on 'Start'. Move the counter one square at a time across or down (but not diagonally) to move around the grid.

For each square you land on, write down the number of 10ps which make that amount. Score this number. Keep moving and adding scores until you reach 'Finish'.

Try to reach 'Finish' with the lowest possible score. Try different routes around the grid. What is the lowest score you can find?

Start			
£0·10	£10·30	£8·60	£0·30
£11·00	£12·20	£7·10	£9·00
£5·50	£14·00	£13·80	£3·90
£10·90	£1·90	£8·40	£0·20
			Finish

In class The children invent their own grids and play again.

Multiplication guess

A person to play with, paper and pencils

Take turns to choose two planet numbers and multiply them in your head. Make jottings to help you if necessary. Write the answer and show your partner.

Your partner must decide which two planet numbers you chose and check the multiplication. Was the guess correct? Did you multiply correctly?

Have six turns each, choosing different pairs of numbers each time.

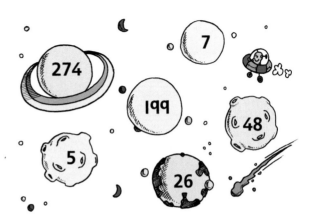

In class Write six numbers on the board. Choose a child to multiply two numbers and say the answer. The others work out which numbers were multiplied.

Area calculations

A ruler or tape measure, paper and pencil

Measure the length and width of two pieces of furniture in your house.

Write their measurements in centimetres. Work out the area of each piece of furniture.

Bed
187 cm long
98 cm wide
187
x 98
_____
_____

In class In pairs, the children measure and work out the area of a table in the classroom.

Looking for 15

A dice, paper and pencil

Throw the dice. Multiply one of the balloon numbers by the number thrown. Choose the balloon number carefully to make the answer as close as possible to 15.

Repeat six times. What is the closest answer to 15 that you can make for each dice number?

In class Write six decimal numbers on the board. The children play the game in pairs with a target answer of 20. Who gets the closest answer?

Who am I?

Paper and pencil

Solve these puzzles, then make up one of your own.

I am a 3-digit number. I am less than 200. When I am divided by 2, 3, 6, 7 or 9, there is a remainder of 1. When I am divided by 8 or 10, there is a remainder of 7. What number am I?

I am a 2-digit number. When I am divided by 2, 3, 4, 5, 6, 7, 8, 9, or 10, the remainder is either 1 or 3. What number am I?

I am a 2-digit number. I can be divided by 4, 6 and 8 with 3 left over. I am divisible by 3 and 11. What number am I?

I am a multiple of 5. When I am divided by 2, 3, 6 or 9, there is a remainder of 1. I am less than 80. What number am I?

In class The children work in pairs to solve each other's puzzles.

Weeks away!

A person to talk to, a calendar or diary, paper and pencil

Write the number of weeks until these dates.

May 1st	The end of term	The birthday of someone you know
Your birthday	New Year's Eve	The start of British summer time

May 1st

11 weeks and

4 days =

$11\frac{4}{7}$ weeks

In class In pairs, the children ask each other the date of their birthdays and work out how many weeks away they are.

In between

A dice, paper and pencil

Throw the dice three times and use the numbers thrown as tenths, hundredths and thousandths. Arrange the digits to make the smallest and the largest 3-place decimal numbers possible.

Rearrange the digits to make two more decimal numbers. Write all the numbers in order.

Repeat ten times.

4, 3, 6

smallest: 0·346

largest: 0·643

0·346<0·436<0·634<0·643

In class In pairs, one child throws the dice three times and makes two 3-place decimal numbers. The other child throws the dice three times and tries to make a number between their partner's numbers.

Seeing stars

A person to play with, paper and pencils

Each choose one line in the star and add up the four numbers along it. Compare the totals. Which is larger? Repeat for different lines of the star. Which line has the largest total? Which has the smallest total?

Look at the five numbers at the points of the star and the five around the central pentagon. Which set do you think will have the largest total? Add them to check.

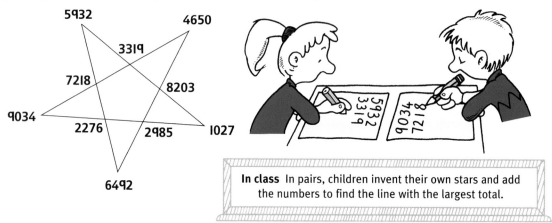

5932   4650
3319
7218   8203
9034
2276   2985   1027
6492

In class In pairs, children invent their own stars and add the numbers to find the line with the largest total.

Receipt race

A person to play with, a calculator, paper and pencils

Look at the first shopping receipt. Write down all the numbers ready to add them. Give your partner the calculator. Race each other to add the numbers. Are you both correct?

Repeat for each receipt in turn. Can you beat the calculator?

Fashion Frenzy				The Sport Store	
boots	£24·78			shin pads	£11·17
t-shirt	£13·21			trainers	£47·39
trousers	£17·08			football	£18·74
skirt	£22·99			tracksuit	£29·02

Beddie Buys		Electric Empire	
pyjamas	£33·77	game	£54·30
teddy	£25·50	video	£12·76
slippers	£27·81	radio	£34·88
nightie	£19·75	earphones	£23·59

In class Write a vertical addition of decimal numbers on the board. Use a calculator to find the total, while the children add the numbers on paper. Can they beat the calculator?

Choose a difference!

> A person to play with, paper and pencils

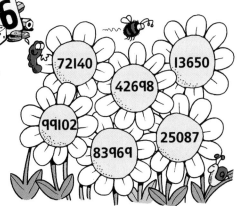

Take turns to choose two flower numbers. Write down a subtraction to subtract the smaller number from the larger. Tell your partner the answer.

Your partner must decide which two flower numbers you chose.

Have three turns each, choosing different pairs of numbers each time.

In class Write six different numbers on the board. Play the game in pairs.

Save or spend?

> A counter or coin, paper and pencil

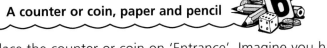

Place the counter or coin on 'Entrance'. Imagine you have saved £150. Move the counter one square at a time across or down (but not diagonally) to move around the department store.

For each square you land on, you buy something in that department costing that amount. Keep moving and subtracting amounts until you reach 'Exit'.

Try to reach 'Exit' with as much of your savings left as possible. Try different routes through the department store. What is the most money you can leave with?

In class In pairs, the children invent their own department store grids. They swap them with their partners and play the game again.

High factor

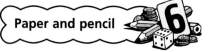

> **Paper and pencil**

Find the number between 1 and 100 with the most factors. List some possibilities and then find the factors for each one. Write down all the factors for each number and count them to check which has the most.

Which number between 100 and 200 has the most factors?

Factors of 18:

1
2
3
6
9
18

In class Discuss which numbers between 200 and 300 might have the most factors.

Family factor tree

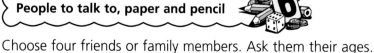

> **People to talk to, paper and pencil**

Choose four friends or family members. Ask them their ages. Draw a factor tree for each age.

Can you draw a factor tree for an age over 50? Whose age has the most prime factors?

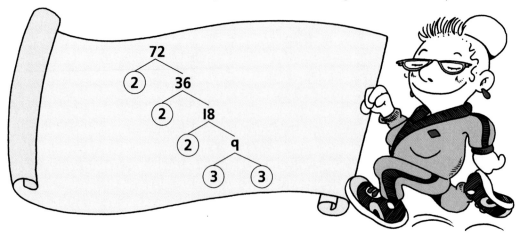

In class Compare factor trees. Which numbers have most branches? Which have least?

Noughts and crosses

A person to play with, paper and pencils

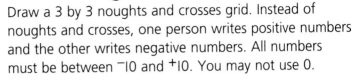

10	⁻6	2
	⁻5	
		5

Draw a 3 by 3 noughts and crosses grid. Instead of noughts and crosses, one person writes positive numbers and the other writes negative numbers. All numbers must be between ⁻10 and ⁺10. You may not use 0.

Take turns to write a number of your type on the board. The first person to complete a straight line of three numbers which add to 0, wins.

Swap types of number and play again. Play ten times. Who wins the most?

In class Play the game, teacher against the class.

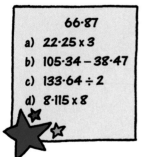

Maths millionaires

A person to play with, a watch or clock, paper and pencils

Imagine you are a contestant on a game show. Start with £1000 prize money.

Your partner chooses a card and reads the number at the top and four different calculations, a, b, c and d. You have 10 seconds to choose the correct calculation. Write it down and then work out each calculation to check.

If you chose correctly, double your prize money and have another turn. If not, start again with £1000. Keep playing until you have answered all the cards. How much prize money did you make?

66·87	74·57	69·44	89·01
a) 22·25 × 3	a) 23·89 × 3	a) 89·6 − 20·16	a) 267·03 ÷ 3
b) 105·34 − 38·47	b) 225·97 ÷ 3	b) 23·12 × 3	b) 111·11 − 22·11
c) 133·64 ÷ 2	c) 94·35 − 19·78	c) 141·8 ÷ 2	c) 17·85 × 5
d) 8·115 × 8	d) 55·49 + 19·18	d) 17·36 × 4	d) 21·54 + 67·74

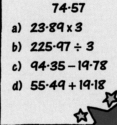
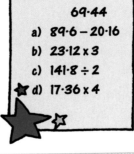

In class Write some different answers and calculations on the board. Play the game with the children working in pairs as contestants. How much do they win?

Seven in a row

> **A person to talk to, a ruler or measuring tape, paper and pencil**

Ask an adult you know to tell you their height in metres. You may have to measure them to check. Write down the height and multiply it by 7.

Write down your own height in metres and multiply it by 7. If seven adults lay down in a row head to toe, how much longer would the line be than a line of seven of you?

> **In class** Compare the lengths of the lines of seven adults. Discuss how long a line of seven dogs or cats might be.

Puzzling pay

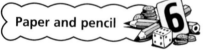

> **Paper and pencil**

Simon has a job delivering papers six days a week. He has a choice of how to be paid. Which do you think gives the best weekly pay?

1 A weekly wage of £15.

2 Daily pay of £2·53.

3 25p on the first day of each week, 50p on the second day, £1 on the third day, with his pay doubling each day throughout the week.

Work out how much Simon would be paid each week for the different methods of payment. Which is best? Was your guess correct?

> **In class** In pairs, the children try to solve the following problem for someone who works six days a week. Which is better: £100 a fortnight, or 25p on the first day, 50p on the second day, £1 on the third day, and so on for a fortnight?

Bubble numbers

A person to play with, paper and pencils

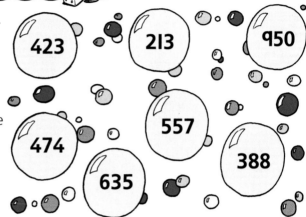

Take turns to choose a bubble number. Divide it by 3, 4, 5, 6, 7 or 8 and write the division, giving the remainder as a fraction. Tell your partner the answer and the number you divided by.

Your partner must decide which bubble number you chose. Are they correct?

Have five turns each, choosing a different bubble number and a different dividing number each time.

In class Write seven different numbers on the board. The children play the game again in pairs.

Lowest to win!

A counter or coin, paper and pencil

Place the counter or coin on 'Start'. Move the counter one square at a time across or down (but not diagonally) to move around the grid.

For each square you land on, divide the amount shown by 3 and score the answer. Keep moving and adding scores until you reach 'Finish'.

Try to reach 'Finish' with as low a score as possible. Try different routes through the grid. What is the lowest total you can score?

Start	£2·61	£4·83	£6·09
£10·41	£8·70	£3·15	£5·73
£4·62	£6·24	£7·71	£8·10
£2·85	£3·69	£4·08	Finish

In class Discuss the lowest possible score. Play again in class, with the children working in pairs to try to find the highest possible score.

Most common letter?

A book, magazine or newspaper, paper and pencil

Open the book, magazine or newspaper at any page and count 100 words. Count how many of these words have the letter 'e' in them. Put a light pencil dot beside them to help you. Write the percentage of words with an 'e'.

Repeat four times counting a different set of 100 words each time. Add together the five percentages and divide the total by 5 to find the average percentage of words with an 'e' in them.

Use a similar method, counting 50 words each time, to find the average percentage of words with a 't' in them.

In class Compare the children's average percentages. What percentage of words have an 'e' in them? What percentage have a 't' in them? Discuss which other letters might be common.

Change percentage

A person with some coins, paper and pencil

Ask someone you know to empty the change out of their pockets or purse. Count how much money they have in total.

Work out these fractions of the total amount. Write each fraction as a percentage.

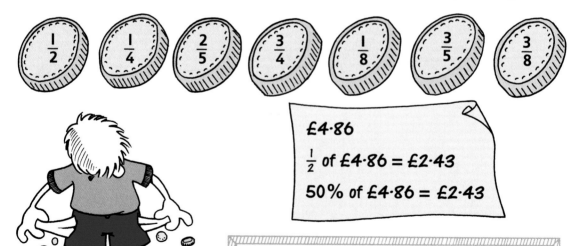

£4·86

$\frac{1}{2}$ of £4·86 = £2·43

50% of £4·86 = £2·43

In class Give each pair a handful of plastic coins. They work out 75%, 35%, and 12·5% of the total amount.

18

Proportion of vowels

A newspaper or magazine, paper and pencil

Look at a newspaper or magazine and choose ten words to underline.

Count the total number of letters in the words. Count the total number of vowels. Work out the proportion of vowels.

Repeat ten times. Compare the proportions. Do they differ much?

In class Discuss whether the proportion of vowels is roughly constant. What is the proportion of consonants?

Ratio race

A person to play with, a dice, coins (10p and 5p), paper and pencils

Each throw the dice and write the two numbers as a ratio.

You take 10p coins to match the first number in the ratio and your partner takes 5p coins to match the second number.
Each work out your amounts and score the total.

Repeat ten times. Who has collected the most money?

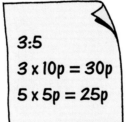

3:5

$3 \times 10p = 30p$

$5 \times 5p = 25p$

In class Play the game in pairs using 20p and 50p coins.

Addition order

> A person to play with, paper, pencils

Take turns to choose six circle numbers. Add the numbers together, writing them in the order in which you add them.

Your partner must add the same numbers in a different order. Do you get the same answer? If not, check again.

Repeat six times, choosing a different set of six circle numbers each time.

12 19 5 23 7 9 25 3 8 32 4 16 18 29

> **In class** Write a set of six numbers on the board in two different orders. Divide the class into two teams. Choose a child from each team to add the numbers. Do they get the same answer? Who finishes fastest?

Checkout check-up

> A shopping receipt, paper and pencil

Use a till receipt from a shopping trip. Copy the prices and check that the total is correct.

Find the reduced number of each price on the receipt and add them all together, finding the reduced number of the answer if necessary. Check that this is the same as the reduced number of the total amount.

$$£2{\cdot}99 \rightarrow 2 + 9 + 9 = 20 \rightarrow 2 + 0 = 2$$
$$£1{\cdot}45 \rightarrow 1 + 4 + 5 = 10 \rightarrow 1 + 0 = 1$$
$$£0{\cdot}75 \rightarrow 0 + 7 + 5 = 12 \rightarrow 1 + 2 = 3$$
$$£3{\cdot}86 \rightarrow 3 + 8 + 6 = 17 \rightarrow 1 + 7 = 8$$
$$£1{\cdot}09 \rightarrow 1 + 0 + 9 = 10 \rightarrow 1 + 0 = 1$$
$$£10{\cdot}14 \rightarrow 1 + 0 + 1 + 4 = \mathbf{6}$$
$$2 + 1 + 3 + 8 + 1 = 15 \rightarrow 1 + 5 = \mathbf{6}$$

> **In class** Write an addition of several numbers on the board. The children check it in pairs using reduced numbers.

Target 1000

A counter or coin, paper and pencil

Place the counter or coin on 'Start'. Move the counter one space at a time across or down (but not diagonally) to move around the grid.

Square each number you land on and score the answer. Keep moving and adding scores until you reach 'Finish'.

Try to reach 'Finish' with a score as close to 1000 as possible. Try different routes through the grid. How close can you get to the target?

Start	20	4	12
21	15	9	25
11	8	10	1
14	7	16	Finish

In class Discuss the closest possible score to 1000. Play again in class, trying to find the highest possible score.

Pocket money pattern

Paper and pencil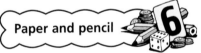

Imagine that your pocket money doubles each day. You get 1p on the first day, 2p on the second day, 4p on the third day, 8p on the fourth day, and so on.

Work out how much pocket money you would get on the twentieth day. How much money would you have in total?

What do you think the total of your pocket money would be on the next day? Check to see if your prediction is correct. What do you notice about the total of the pocket money each day?

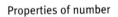

Day	Pocket Money	Total
1	1p	1p
2	2p	3p
3	4p	7p
4	8p	

In class Discuss the patterns. Can the children write a rule to predict the amount of pocket money received on any day, and the total amount?

Even more evens

 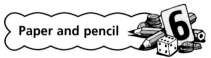

Paper and pencil

Work out how many even numbers there are between these numbers.

1 and 100   100 and 200

200 and 300   1 and 1000   1 and 10 000

How many odd numbers are there?

In class Check the answers. Discuss the methods the children used to work them out.

Lengthy discussions

Length **M1**

A person to talk to, paper and pencil

Find out the distance from where you live to ten different places. Write the distances in miles. What would be the best way to travel to each place?

Convert all the distances into kilometres. Bring your calculations into school.

Home → Moon

about 250,000 miles

about 400,000 km

In class Discuss some of the examples the children chose and whether the suggested methods of transport are appropriate.

Which weights?

> A pair of weighing scales, items to weigh, paper and pencil

Find five items to weigh on the weighing scales.
Write the weight of each in pounds and ounces.

Convert the weights into kilograms and grams.

Repeat, weighing five
different items in
kilograms and grams.
Convert the weights
into pounds and ounces.

1 oz ≈ 25 g

In class Discuss the weights of different common objects, e.g. a bag of sugar.

Liquid assets

> A person to talk to, containers of different liquids (shampoo,
> milk, cola, washing-up liquid, …), a calculator, paper and pencil

Find several different bottles, cans or cartons containing liquids. Look at each bottle
and write how much liquid it contains. Write each capacity in millilitres. Convert the
capacities into pints.

Ask someone you know the price of each bottle. Can you work out how much one
millilitre of each liquid costs? Which liquid costs the most per millilitre? Which costs
the least? How much does each liquid cost per pint?

In class Compare the different liquids. Which are expensive? Which are cheap?

Surface area

> **A ruler or measuring tape, paper and pencil**

Find two pieces of furniture with rectangular sides. Which do you think has a larger surface area?

Measure the length and breadth of each side of the first piece of furniture in centimetres, and write them down. Calculate the area of each side in square centimetres. Work out the total surface area of the piece of furniture. Repeat for the second piece of furniture.

Compare the surface areas. Which is larger? Was your guess correct?

In class Measure some items in the classroom. In pairs, the children find the surface area of the items.

Triangle teaser

> **A ruler, squared paper and pencil**

Draw a right-angled triangle.

Measure its sides and work out the area of the triangle.

Can you draw another triangle with the same area but different length sides?

In class Discuss how the children drew their triangles. Did they all use the same method to find them?

Initial edges

> **A ruler, string, paper and pencil**

Draw your initials as large as possible on a piece of squared paper.

Calculate the perimeter of each letter. Use a ruler to measure letters with straight edges and a piece of string to measure letters with curved edges.

In class Discuss which letters have the longest perimeter and which have the shortest.

Shapely angles

> **A ruler, a protractor, squared paper and pencil**

Draw these shapes with one interior angle of more than 180°.

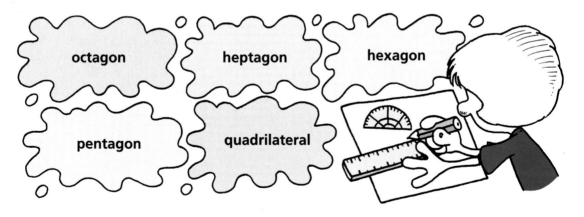

octagon

heptagon

hexagon

pentagon

quadrilateral

Which of the these shapes can you draw with two interior angles of more than 180°?
Which can be drawn with three interior angles of more than 180°?

In class Compare the children's drawings. Discuss which shapes can be drawn with more than three interior angles of more than 180°.

Triangle angles

Paper and pencil

Calculate the missing angles, a, b, c, d and e, and write them on your paper.

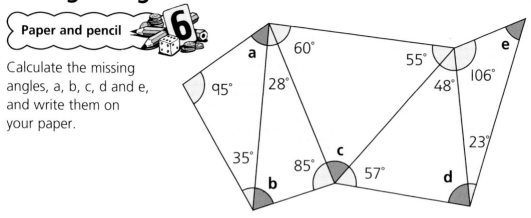

In class The children design their own pattern of triangles. They use a protractor to measure two of the angles, then swap with a partner to calculate the third angle in each triangle.

Map work

Squared paper and pencil

Draw two axes at right-angles and label both from ⁻10 to 10.

Draw a map of an island on your grid. Include several landmarks or objects at different points on your grid. Write the coordinates of ten places on the map.

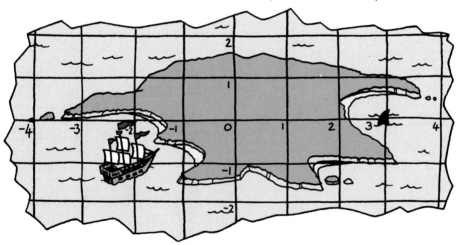

In class The children work in pairs. They each hide a piece of treasure on their map and ask each other questions to discover its position. Is the first coordinate positive? Is the second coordinate negative? The first child to locate their partner's treasure wins.

Mirror images

> A small mirror, a ruler, coloured pencils, squared paper and pencil

Draw an interesting shape on squared paper. Colour the squares to make a complicated pattern.

Hold your shape next to a mirror to help you draw its reflection. Take care that you draw the reflection accurately.

> **In class** Compare the chidren's shapes. In pairs, the children swap shapes, draw the mirror line on their partner's shape and check that the reflection is accurate.

Translations

> A ruler, squared paper and pencil

Draw two axes to make a coordinate grid on squared paper.
Label them both from ⁻10 to 10.

Draw a shape in the top right-hand quadrant.
Draw the position of the shape after these translations.

> **5 units left and 2 units up**

> **5 units left and 2 units down**

> **2 units right and 10 units down**

Can you describe some more translations to make an interesting pattern with the shape?

> **In class** Compare translations. Which shapes make the best patterns? Draw four identical shapes in different quadrants of a coordinate grid. Discuss the translations needed to move between them.

Flexicubes

> A piece of card, scissors, a ruler, glue, tracing paper and pencil

Trace this net onto a piece of card.

Cut out the shape and crease all the diagonals. Fold the card and glue the tab to the opposite end to make an open cube.

When the glue has dried, try turning the cube inside out.

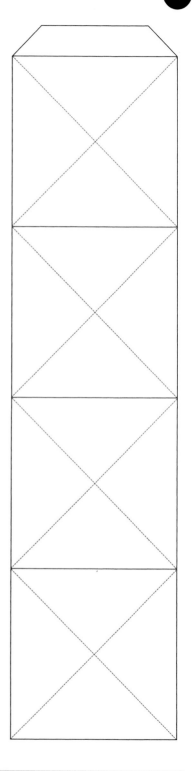

In class The children use their flexicubes to demonstrate how to turn the cube inside out!

Parallelograms

A ruler marked in cm, cm-squared paper and pencil

Draw a rectangle on squared paper 4 cm high and 6 cm long.
Write the perimeter of the rectangle.

Draw a parallelogram of the same height as the rectangle by moving
the top side I cm to the right.

Measure the perimeter of the parallelogram.

Draw four more parallelograms in this way, moving the top line I cm to the right each
time. Measure all the perimeters. What do you notice?

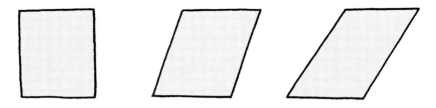

In class Look at the patterns of the perimeters. How does the perimeter of the parallelograms increase?

Kites

A ruler, a protractor, squared paper and pencil

On squared paper draw these shapes.

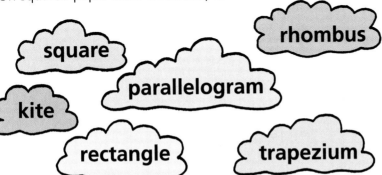

square **rhombus** **parallelogram** **kite** **rectangle** **trapezium**

Draw the diagonals for each shape. Measure the angle where the diagonals cross.
What do you notice?

In class Look at the diagonals. Can we predict what the angle
of intersection of the diagonals will be for each shape?

Nested shapes

A ruler, colouring pencils, paper and pencil

Draw a 2-d shape. Draw a different shape around it. Draw another shape around this shape, and so on.

Continue until you have drawn eight different nested shapes.

Label each shape with its correct name.
Colour the shapes to make an interesting pattern.

In class Do a class survey to find which shapes were most popular. Draw the most popular shape on the board, then the next most popular, and so on. Draw these as nested shapes.

TV time

A current TV guide, paper and pencil

Look at the TV guide for tonight and work out how long each programme between 5 p.m. and 11 p.m. lasts in minutes.

Draw a grouped frequency table for programmes lasting these numbers of minutes.

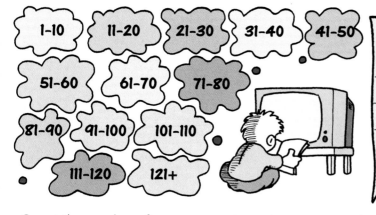

Length of programme in minutes	Number of programmes
1–10	2
11–20	1
21–30	
31–40	

1–10   11–20   21–30   31–40   41–50
51–60   61–70   71–80
81–90   91–100   101–110
111–120   121+

Count the number of programmes in each category and mark them in the frequency table. Bring your frequency table into class.

In class Collect together all of the children's results and draw a graph on the board to show the data. What length of programme occurs most frequently?

Car of the year

A person to help you, a circular plate, a ruler, a protractor, paper and pencil

Look at some parked cars near where you live. Write down the different makes of car you see. Survey 24 cars and draw a tally chart to show how many cars there are of each different make.

Draw round a plate to make a pie chart. Use a ruler and protractor to split the circle into 24 sections. Each section should be 15°.

Colour and label the pie chart to show your data about the cars.

In class Compare the children's pie charts. Collect the information into one table and draw a class pie chart. Which make of car is most common?

Exchange rates

A table of currency conversion rates, a ruler, squared paper and pencil

Look at a currency conversion table in a newspaper, bank or travel agency.

Choose a foreign currency. Write how many of the unit of this currency equal one pound. Draw a conversion graph from £0 to £100, marking the horizontal axis in £10 intervals.

In class Compare the children's graphs, and discuss the different currencies. Draw a graph on the board to show the Euro against the pound.

Beauty sleep

> A person to talk to, calculator, paper and pencil

How many hours do you sleep each night? Write the times you go to bed and the times you get up each weekday for one week. Work out how long you slept each night to the nearest half hour and draw a chart to show the data.

Use a calculator to work out the mean number of hours you slept each night. Find the mode and the median.

Ask an adult you know how many hours they sleep each night. Draw a chart and calculate the mean, mode and median number of hours.

On average how much longer do you sleep?

Day	Go to bed	Get up	Hours
Monday	9 p.m.	7 a.m.	10
Tuesday	8:30 p.m.	7 a.m.	10·5
Wednesday	9:30 p.m.		

> **In class** Compare their averages. Discuss the different times children and adults sleep. Which way of finding an average seems the most sensible in this case?

Heads or tails

> A 10p coin, paper and pencil

How many times do you think you will get heads if you toss or spin a coin twenty times? How many times do you think you will get tails? Write down your predictions.

Now toss or spin a coin twenty times.
Record the results in a tally chart.

Look at the results. How many times
did you throw heads? How many times did you throw tails?

Repeat twice more. Are the results the same?

> **In class** Compare the children's results. Do they match the predictions? Why not?